ARISTOTLE CONTEMPLATING THE BUST OF HOMER

REMBRANDT

The COLLECTION *of* TWENTY-FOUR

Old Master Paintings

FORMED BY THE LATE

Mr *and* Mrs Alfred W. Erickson

By Order of

BANKERS TRUST COMPANY, NEW YORK, *Trustee* FOR THE
ANNA E. ERICKSON TRUST; AND EARL A. DARR AND
BANKERS TRUST COMPANY, *Executors of Her Estate*

PUBLIC AUCTION

Wednesday Evening · November 15 at 8 o'clock

ADMISSION TO SALE BY CARD ONLY
To be Obtained by Application to the Galleries

FREE PUBLIC EXHIBITION

Saturday & Monday, November 11 and 13 · From 10 to 5 p. m.
Tuesday, November 14 · From 10 to 8 p. m.
No Exhibition on Day of Sale

SALE NUMBER 2062

PARKE-BERNET GALLERIES · INC

980 Madison Avenue · New York
1961

BIOGRAPHICAL MEMOIR

---❋---

ALFRED W. ERICKSON *(1876-1936) was of Swedish descent, and was born at Farmers Mills, New York. He was educated in Brooklyn, and at the age of twenty-four began a long association with the advertising business that culminated in the establishment of the Erickson Advertising Agency, which in 1930 joined with H. K. McCann Company, forming McCann-Erickson, Inc., with Mr Erickson as Chairman of the Board. He was a pioneer in the organization of the advertising field into an association, and in the formation of codes of ethics governing its practices; and as a result of his external business activities was a director of numerous companies and became Chairman of the Board of Congoleum-Nairn, Inc. He was a close friend and great admirer of Theodore Roosevelt, and was a Trustee of the Roosevelt Memorial Association.*

In the 1920's he began, with his wife Anna, to assemble the collection of paintings which was to achieve a reputation on both sides of the Atlantic, and which has been viewed over the years by art experts from many of the major countries of the western world. The collection was little known to the general public; subsequent to Mr Erickson's death, his widow acquired a few paintings of importance, and continued to enrich her knowledge in the art field by interrogating her advisers and the experts who called upon her, until her death in February 1961. The range of the paintings indicates the Ericksons' catholicity of taste, and their determination to bring together a collection which would, in essence, hypostatize in large measure the development of painting from the quattrocento *to the end of the eighteenth century.*

The Parke-Bernet Galleries

will execute your bids without charge
if you are unable to attend the sale in person
Telephone: Trafalgar 9-8300
Cable: Parkgal

CONDITIONS OF SALE

The property listed in this catalogue will be offered and sold on the following terms and conditions:

1. The word "Galleries," whenever here used, means the Parke-Bernet Galleries, Inc.

2. The Galleries has endeavored to catalogue and describe the property correctly, but all property is sold "as is" and neither the Galleries nor its consignor warrants or represents, and they shall in no event be responsible for, the correctness of description, genuineness, authorship, provenience or condition of the property, and no statement contained in the catalogue or made orally at the sale or elsewhere shall be deemed to be such a warranty or representation, or an assumption of liability.

3. Unless otherwise announced by the auctioneer at the time of sale, all bids are to be for a single article even though more than one article is included under a numbered item in the catalogue. If, however, all of the articles under a numbered item are either specifically designated by the auctioneer at the time of the sale or designated in the printed catalogue as a "Lot," then bids are to be for the lot irrespective of the number of items. However, in book catalogues, *all* bids are to be for the lot as numbered, unless specific notification to the contrary is given by the auctioneer at the time of sale.

4. The highest bidder acknowledged by the auctioneer shall be the purchaser. In the event of any dispute between bidders, the auctioneer shall have absolute discretion either to determine the successful bidder, in which event his determination shall be final, or to re-offer and resell the article in dispute. If any dispute arises after the sale, the Galleries' sale record shall be conclusive as to who was the purchaser, the amount of the highest bid, and in all other respects.

5. If, the auctioneer, in his sole and final discretion, decides that any original bid is not commensurate with the value of the article offered, or, having acknowledged an original bid, that any advance thereafter is not of sufficient amount, he may reject the same.

6. The name and address of the purchaser of each article or lot shall be given to the Galleries immediately following the sale thereof, and payment of the whole purchase price, or such part thereof as the Galleries may require, shall be made immediately by the purchaser. If the foregoing condition, or any other applicable condition herein, is not complied with, the sale may, at the option of the Galleries, be cancelled and the article or lot re-offered for sale.

7. Unless the sale is advertised and announced as an unrestricted sale, or as a sale without reserve, the consignor has reserved the right to bid personally or by agent; and if the consignor or his agent is the highest bidder, less than full commissions may, under certain defined circumstances, be payable.

8. Except as otherwise provided in paragraph 6 hereof, title will pass to the highest bidder upon the fall of the auctioneer's hammer, and thereafter, the purchaser shall bear the sole risk and responsibility for the property.

9. All property purchased is to be paid for in full and removed from the Galleries at the purchaser's risk and expense immediately after the conclusion of the sale. As to any property not so paid for in full, in addition to all other remedies available to the Galleries by law, including, without limitation, the right to hold the purchaser

liable for the bid price, the Galleries, at its option, may either (a) cancel the sale, in which event all payments made by the purchaser shall be retained as liquidated damages, or (b) resell the same without notice to the purchaser and for the purchaser's account and risk, either publicly or privately, and, in such event, the purchaser shall be liable for the payment of any deficiency plus all costs, including warehousing, the expenses of both sales, and the Galleries' commissions at its regular rates. All property not promptly removed by the purchaser may be removed by the Galleries to a warehouse for the account and risk and at the expense of the purchaser.

10. Items or categories in this catalogue which are subject to the Federal Excise Tax on jewelry, clocks, silver, gold, furs, etc., are designated by an asterisk (*). Unless acquired by a registered dealer for resale the purchaser will be required to pay in addition to the amount of his bid, the Federal Excise Tax equivalent to 10 per cent of the bid.

11. Unless exempt from the payment thereof, the purchaser will also be required to pay the New York City sales tax of 3 per cent of the bid.

12. The Galleries, without charge for its services, may undertake to make bids on behalf of responsible persons approved by it, including the consignor, subject to the Conditions of Sale and to such other terms and conditions as it may prescribe. The Galleries reserves the right, however, to decline to undertake to make such bids and when undertaking to make such bids shall in no event be responsible for failing correctly to carry out instructions.

13. The Galleries, at the purchaser's risk and expense, will facilitate the employment of carriers and packers for the purchaser's account, but will not be responsible for their acts in any respect whatsoever.

14. Any and all claims of a purchaser shall be deemed to be waived and shall be without validity unless made in writing to the Galleries within ten days after the sale.

15. Neither the auctioneer nor any other representative of the Galleries shall have the authority to waive or alter, in whole or in part, any of these Conditions of Sale, or except as provided in paragraphs 6 and 9 hereof, orally to cancel any sale.

Sales Conducted by

LOUIS J. MARION

WILLIAM A. SMYTH · THEODORE J. MULDOON

CHARLES A. HELLMICH

PARKE-BERNET GALLERIES · INC

LESLIE A. HYAM · *President*

LOUIS J. MARION · *Executive Vice-President*

MARY VANDEGRIFT · ANTHONY N. BADE · *Vice-President*

MAX BARTHOLET · *Secretary & Treasurer*

ROBERT F. METZDORF · *Assistant Vice-President*

CATALOGUE

LIST OF ARTISTS

———————※———————

NUMBER ONE

Jan Mostaert

Portrait of a Man

JAN MOSTAERT   NETHERLANDISH: 1475-1555/6

1. *PORTRAIT OF A MAN*. Waist-length figure, gazing to half-right, of a man wearing a flat black cap, a gray watered silk coat with fur collar, brilliant scarlet and black doublet and a white pleated shirt; shaded green background.

Arched panel: 18¼ x 12¼ inches

Note: Dr. Max Friedländer, in an interesting article in the *Repertorium* (*vide infra*) of 1905, defined and enlarged the *oeuvre of* Jan Mostaert, whom he identifies with the Master of the Oultremont Altar. He speaks of the present picture and its companion (no. 2) as "characteristic of Mostaert in delicate, clean painting. . . . Judging from the dress, probably not painted before 1520."

Companion to the following

Painted about 1520-30

Private Collection, Wiesbaden, *c.* 1904

Collection of Richard von Kaufmann, Berlin, 1917 (cat. edit. by Dr. Max Friedländer)

From Goudstikker, Amsterdam

Described by Dr. Max Friedländer in *Repertorium für Kunstwissenschaft*, 1905, vol. 28, p. 518

Recorded by Dr. Max Friedländer in *Onze Kunst*, 1906, vol. 5, no. 8, p. 39

Recorded in Max J. Friedländer, *Die Altniederländische Malerei*, 1934, vol. X, p. 124, no. 46

2

PORTRAIT OF A MAN

MOSTAERT

NUMBER TWO

JAN MOSTAERT

Portrait of a Lady

JAN MOSTAERT   NETHERLANDISH: 1475-1555/6

2. *PORTRAIT OF A LADY*. Half-length figure, turned to half-left, wearing a white wimple and brown stole over a black jerkin; her hands are clasped before her; green background.   *Arched panel: 18¼ x 12¼ inches*

See note to the preceding.

Companion to the preceding

Painted about 1520-30

Private Collection, Wiesbaden, *c.* 1904

Collection of Richard von Kaufmann, Berlin, 1917 (cat. edit. by Dr. Max Friedländer)

From Goudstikker, Amsterdam

Described by Dr. Max Friedländer in *Repertorium für Kunstwissenschaft,* 1905, vol. 28, p. 518

Recorded by Dr. Max Friedländer in *Onze Kunst,* 1906, vol. 5, no. 8, p. 39

Recorded in Max Friedländer, *Die Altniederländische Malerei,* 1934, vol. X, p. 124, no. 46

PORTRAIT OF A LADY

MOSTAERT

NUMBER THREE

Sir Anthony Van Dyck

Portrait of a Genoese Officer

SIR ANTHONY VAN DYCK   FLEMISH: 1599-1641

3. *PORTRAIT OF A GENOESE OFFICER.* Three-quarter-length figure of a bearded nobleman, turned to half-left, wearing gold-trimmed polished black half-armor, his left hand resting on the hilt of his rapier. An old inscription on the back of the canvas reads: *Antonio van dyck Genuae 1626.*   45½ x 38½ inches

Painted about 1622-27

Collection of Robert Townley Parker, Esq.

Collection of Capt. T. A. Tatton, M.C., Guerdon Hall, Preston, Lancs.

From Duveen Bros., Inc., New York

Recorded and illustrated in Gustav Glück, *Van Dyck (Klassiker der Kunst)*, 1931, no. 169

Mentioned in Leo van Puyvelde, *Van Dyck*, 1950, p. 60

PORTRAIT OF A GENOESE OFFICER

VAN DYCK

NUMBER FOUR

Gerard Terborch

Aelbert Nilant

$ 22000

GERARD TERBORCH   DUTCH: 1617-1681

4. *AELBERT NILANT*. Standing full-length figure of a man, turned to half-right, wearing a black doublet over a white blouse with broad lawn collar, and pleated black apron or skirt; in his left hand he holds a broad-brimmed black hat.

Panel: 28 x 20 inches

Aelbert Nilant (b. 1646) was the Treasurer of Ter Hunnep, and married in 1676 Alida Bannier (d. 1685), daughter of Frederick Fredericks Bannier, husband of Johanna Quadacker, the subject of the companion portrait in the present catalogue (no. 5); they had three children who died young, and the portrait passed, after the sitter's death, into the possession of the Bannier family.

Companion to the following

Painted about 1660-62

Collection of the Bannier family of Deventer

Collection of M. E. Houck, Deventer, 1864, no. 9

Collection of J. H. Houck, Amsterdam, 1895, no. 54

From P. & D. Colnaghi, London

Collection of Beryold Richter, Berlin

Collection of Joseph Block, Berlin

From the Bachstitz Gallery, The Hague

Exhibited at the John Herron Art Institute, Indianapolis, Ind., 1937, no. 68

Recorded in Hofstede de Groot, *Catalogue Raisonné*, 1913, vol. V, no. 250

Recorded and illustrated in S. J. Gudlaugsson, *Katalog der Gemälde Gerard Ter Borchs*, 1960, no. 176

AELBERT NILANT

TERBORCH

NUMBER FIVE

GERARD TERBORCH

Johanna Quadacker Bannier

GERARD TERBORCH   DUTCH: 1617-1681

5. *JOHANNA QUADACKER BANNIER.* Standing full-length figure of a woman, turned to half-left, wearing a long black gown enhanced with a white lace cape collar and *manchettes;* in her clasped hands is a closed fan.   28 x 20 *inches*

Johanna Quadacker (1640-1672) married in 1657 Frederick Fredericks Bannier, and with her husband died in 1672, of the plague. Her daughter Alida was married in 1676 to Aelbert Nilant, the sitter of the preceding painting.

Since the Houck sale in 1895, the portrait, according to Gudlaugsson, has erroneously been known as *Swaentje Nilant* (1653-1724). Its correct identification was established by comparison with another portrait of the same subject inscribed on the back with the name of Johanna Quadacker, wife of Fr. Fr. Bannier. The artist himself was a distant connection by marriage of the sitter.

Companion to the preceding

Painted about 1658-60

Collection of the Bannier family of Deventer

Collection of M. E. Houck, Deventer, 1864, no. 10

Collection of J. H. Houck, Amsterdam, 1895, no. 55

From P. & D. Colnaghi, London

From Charles Sedelmeyer, Paris

Collection of James Simon, Berlin

From K. Haberstock, Berlin

From the Bachstitz Gallery, The Hague

Exhibited at Berlin, 1909, no. 141

Exhibited at the John Herron Art Institute, Indianapolis, Ind., 1937, no. 69, illus. in the catalogue

Recorded in Hofstede de Groot, *Catalogue Raisonné,* 1913, vol. v, no. 253 (*as Swaentje Nilant*)

Recorded and illustrated in S. J. Gudlaugsson, *Katalog der Gemälde Gerard Ter Borchs,* 1960, no. 175

JOHANNA QUADACKER BANNIER

TERBORCH

NUMBER SIX

Lucas Cranach the Elder

Princess Sibylle of Cleves, Electress of Saxony

LUCAS CRANACH THE ELDER SAXON: 1472-1553

6. *PRINCESS SIBYLLE OF CLEVES, ELECTRESS OF SAXONY.* Three-quarter-length figure of a young woman with long auburn hair, wearing an elaborately jeweled and puffed forest green velvet gown, with a large gold brooch about her neck and a delicate jeweled wreath with a feather, on her head; black background. Signed at lower right with the serpent symbol. *Cradled panel: 20¾ x 15 inches*

Princess Sibylle (1510-1554) was a sister of Anne of Cleves, one of the wives of Henry VIII of England; in 1526 she married Johann Friedrich I, Elector of Saxony, called "The Magnanimous." Cranach was court painter to this ruler, even using his influence to secure the Elector's release from prison after the battle of Mühlberg in 1547.

The princess was an early advocate of the Reformation, and was a friend of Luther. The couple's marriage was marked by many interruptions and troubles due to the religious wars; at her death she was buried in the parish church at Weimar.

Note: Another, very similar portrait of Princess Sibylle by Cranach is in the Weimar Museum and is illustrated in Friedländer and Rosenberg, *Die Gemälde von Lucas Cranach,* 1932, no. 244. Dr. Max Friedländer has written of the present picture, which he saw too late for inclusion in his *catalogue raisonné:* "The painting is in my opinion an original in good condition, painted by Lucas Cranach, The Elder, about 1525."——Berlin, August 24, 1937. A typescript copy of this statement is contained in a brochure which will be given to the purchaser.

Painted probably for her marriage in 1525-26

Collection von Mendelssohn, Berlin

From M. Knoedler & Co., Inc., New York

PRINCESS SIBYLLE OF CLEVES

CRANACH

REMBRANDT HARMENSZ VAN RIJN   DUTCH: 1606-1669

7. ARISTOTLE CONTEMPLATING THE BUST OF HOMER. The philosopher, wearing a broad-brimmed black hat, and with a golden yellow mantle draped over his dark robes, stands at three-quarter-length gazing down to left at a sculptured marble bust of the blind poet, which rests on a table before him. He wears a golden chain with a pendant portrait medallion of Alexander the Great, his most famous pupil. Behind the group hangs a drapery partly concealing a pile of books. Signed on the base of the bust REMBRANDT *f.*, and dated 1653.   56½ x 53¾ *inches*

Note: The genesis of this picture forms part of one of the most curious events of Rembrandt's life. In the 'fifties, his popularity as a painter had declined sharply in Holland, and he was entering on a period of financial straits which culminated in the cession of his possessions to his creditors in July 1656, and the forced sale of his collection of paintings, including a number of his own works. Nevertheless, his fame had spread widely through Europe; and in 1652, Don Antonio Ruffo, a Sicilian nobleman of Messina, wrote to the painter and commissioned from him the present painting, which was completed in 1653, and delivered in the following year. It may be noted that the bust of Homer shown in the picture is mentioned in Rembrandt's own inventory; it was probably a cast of the original, which is in the Naples Museum.

In the *Bolletino d'Arte* of 1916, appeared an extended study written by the Marquis Vincenzo Ruffo of the history of the vast collection of paintings once owned by his family; and from the surviving documents he published, among other historical material of the time, the full story of his ancestor's transactions with Rembrandt, from which we extract the data which follow.

As indicated above, the painting ordered from Rembrandt was delivered in 1654; the Marquis was so pleased with this work, which was christened *Aristotle,* that he decided to have two companion pieces executed by the Italian painters Guercino and Preti; and the former went so far as to paint for him *a Cosmographer,* in which the subject is shown contemplating a globe, this being Guercino's concept of a suitable companion to the *Aristotle,* which he took to represent a 'physiognomist.'

The Marquis then changed his mind and decided to order the two additional paintings from Rembrandt himself; and the painter sent him in 1661 an *Alexander the Great,* and in 1662 a *Homer,* the latter of which was returned to be changed at the owner's request. The two last pictures dropped from sight during the ultimate dispersal of the Ruffo collections, and present authorities can only speculate on their identity with various known works (e.g. Dr. Bredius' *Homer* at The Hague, which is actually dated 1663, and is published by him as being the Ruffo picture). The last known appearance of the *Alexander* occurred when the collection as a whole passed in 1743 to a cadet branch of the family, owing to the death of the older members from the plague; this picture became alienated from the estate and was sold at auction in Amsterdam on June 5, 1765.

Further details of interest concerning the *Aristotle* include the fact that the intermediary by which it was delivered was a certain Cornelius Eysbert van Goor of Amsterdam; the cost of the painting was five hundred florins, and of the packing, weighing, transportation, etc., fl. 15.85. The correspondence also indicates

[Continued

26

the manner in which the payments could be remitted, as prescribed by the agent van Goor. The painting was carried from Texel to Naples in the ship *Bartholomeus,* and then transported from Naples to Messina.

The *Aristotle* seems to have left the Ruffo collection during the lordship of Don Giovanni, who became the head of the family about 1760; and it was already in the well-known collection of Sir Abraham Hume at the beginning of the nineteenth century. At this time, the history and title had become obscured, and it was known throughout the century under different names *(vide infra);* as late as 1910, the subject was variously styled in the considerable Rembrandt literature.

Painted for the Marquis Antonio Ruffo in 1652-53 *(vide supra)*

Collection of the Ruffo family of Messina, Sicily

Collection of Don Giovanni Ruffo e la Rocca, Messina, *c.* 1760

Collection of Sir Abraham Hume, Bart., Ashridge Park, Herts., before 1815

Collection of Earl Brownlow, Ashridge Park, Herts., his son-in-law

Collection of Rodolphe Kann, Paris, cat. no. 65 (*as* Portrait of a Savant)

From Duveen Bros., Inc., New York

Collection of Mrs Collis P. Huntington, New York

From Duveen Bros., Inc., New York, 1928

Exhibited at the British Institution, London, 1815, no. 39 (*as* Portrait of Pieter Cornelius van Hooft)

Royal Academy Winter Exhibition, London, 1893, no. 125 (*as* Portrait of a Man)

Dutch Masters Exhibition, Hudson-Fulton Celebration, Metropolitan Museum of Art, New York, 1909, no. 97, illus. in the catalogue (*as* The Savant)

Rembrandt Exhibition, Detroit Institute of Arts, Detroit, Mich., 1930, no. 51, illus. in the catalogue

Art Treasures Exhibition, London, 1932, no. 1355, illus, in the catalogue

Tercentennial Exhibition of the University of Amsterdam, Rijksmuseum, Amsterdam, 1932, no. 26, illus. in the catalogue

Century of Progress Exhibition, Art Institute of Chicago, Chicago, Ill., 1933, no. 73, illus. in the catalogue, pl. xxxiii

Exhibition, Allied Art for Allied Aid, Knoedler Galleries, New York, 1940, no. 5, illus. in the catalogue

Loan Exhibition in Honor of Royal Cortissoz, Knoedler Galleries, New York, 1941, no. 16, illus. in the catalogue

Recorded in C. Vosmaer, *Rembrandt, Sa Vie et Ses Oeuvres,* 1877, p. 551

[*Continued*

Number Seven—Concluded]

Recorded in Dutuit, *L'Oeuvre Complet de Rembrandt,* 1881-85, vol. III, p 43

Recorded in Emile Michel, *Rembrandt,* 1893, p. 555

Recorded and illustrated in W. von Bode and C. Hofstede de Groot, *The Complete Works of Rembrandt,* 1901, vol. v, no. 385, pl. opp. p. 184

Recorded and illustrated in W. Valentiner, *Rembrandt, Des Meisters Gemälde (Klassiker der Kunst),* 1908, no. 426 (*as* Virgil)

Recorded in C. Hofstede de Groot, *Catalogue Raisonné,* 1916, vol. VI, no. 413 (*as* A Bearded Man Before a Bust of Homer)

Described by Vincenzo Ruffo, *La Galleria Ruffo . . . Secolo XVII,* in *Bolletino d'Arte,* 1916

Described and illustrated in Corrado Ricci, *Rembrandt in Italia,* 1918, p. 8ff.

Described and illustrated in W. R. Valentiner, *Rembrandt Paintings in America,* 1931, no. 115

Illustrated in *The Art Digest,* May 1933

Illustrated in *Art News,* May 1933

Recorded and illustrated in A. Bredius, *The Paintings of Rembrandt* (Phaidon ed.) [1942], no. 478

Recorded and illustrated in Jakob Rosenberg, *Rembrandt,* 1948, pp. 165-68, 198, fig. 242

Described in Seymour Slive, *Rembrandt and His Critics,* 1953, pp. 59-62

Mentioned in Otto Benesch, *Rembrandt* (Skira 'Taste of Our Time' series), 1957, pp. 91, 93, 96

Described and illustrated in *Rembrandt* (Phaidon ed.), 1960, no. 77

[See also frontispiece in color]

ARISTOTLE CONTEMPLATING THE BUST OF HOMER

REMBRANDT

NUMBER EIGHT

Hans Holbein the Younger

Sir George Nevill, 5th Lord Bergavenny

HANS HOLBEIN THE YOUNGER GERMAN: 1497/8-1543

8. *SIR GEORGE NEVILL, 5TH LORD BERGAVENNY*. Bust portrait to half-right of a gentleman wearing a flat black velvet cap ornamented with a jewel, and a black robe trimmed with brown fur and the George of the Order of the Garter; emerald green background. *Cradled panel: 16 x 11½ inches*

Sir George Nevill, 5th Lord Bergavenny, was born in July 1483, and was the oldest son of George, 4th Lord and Margaret, daughter of Sir Hugh Fenne, Under-Treasurer of England. He was created a Knight of the Bath at the coronation of Richard III; under Henry VII he distinguished himself against the Cornish Rebels at Blackheath in 1497, and became the companion-in-arms of Henry VIII during the French wars. This monarch also invested him with the Garter and gave him many important commands. He was summoned to Parliament in the twenty-first year of Henry VIII's reign as "George Nevyle de Bergavenny, Chivaler." He served as Privy Councillor in 1515, and at the coronation of Anne Boleyn, he acted as Chief Larderer. He died in the twenty-seventh year of Henry VIII's reign, and was succeeded by his eldest son Henry.

In the seventeenth century the name *Bergavenny* became *Abergavenny* and the spelling of the family name *Neville*, instead of *Nevill*.

Note: Dr. Paul Ganz of Basel, the foremost expert on Holbein, wrote concerning this picture under date Feb. 27, 1926, as follows: "The portrait of George Neville, third Lord Abergavenny [sic] is a genuine work by Hans Holbein the Younger. The sketch for this picture exists now in the collection of the Earl of Pembroke in Wiltonhouse. It was drawn in colored chalk on red paper between 1533 and 1535, at the period when Holbein painted his finest pictures in England and when he was at the climax of his artistic glory." This MS opinion will be given to the purchaser.

In the first complete edition of his work *The Paintings of Hans Holbein* (1956), Dr. Ganz writes further of the picture as follows: "The portrait painted from it [the Wilton drawing] exists in many versions. . . . The version illustrated here [the Erickson picture] is the best known today; although it is by no means preserved in its original condition, it does show Holbein's art both in the general conception and in details."

Painted about 1533-35

Collection of the Earls of Abergavenny

Collection of Thomas Lord Wotton, one of whose ancestors was a son-in-law of the sitter

Collection of the Earl of Stanhope, Boughton Malherbe, Kent

From Duveen Bros., Inc., New York

Described and illustrated in Paul Ganz, *The Paintings of Hans Holbein* (Phaidon ed.) 1956, pp. 243-44, no. 75, fig. 22

GEORGE NEVILL, 5TH LORD BERGAVENNY

HOLBEIN

NUMBER NINE

CARLO CRIVELLI

Madonna and Child

CARLO CRIVELLI   VENETIAN: 1430-1493/5

9. *MADONNA AND CHILD.* The Virgin, wearing a brocaded gold mantle of Gothic pattern lined in vivid emerald green, over a crimson gown, is seated upon a marble throne; in her lap stands the Child, in plain golden robe, who gestures animatedly to the right; on the fissured base of the throne are two figs and an insect. Gold *bulino* background. Signed at lower left + CAROLVS + CRIVELLVS + VENETVS + PIN-SIT +, and dated 1472. In carved 'tabernacle' frame.

Tempera on arched panel: 41 x 17¼ inches

> *Note:* Bernard Berenson, in *Italian Pictures of the Renaissance (Venetian School)* vol. I, pl. 137, has brought together for the first time in a single illustration the great polyptych of 1472, of which the present picture is the central panel. The left wing panels depict *S. Nicholas of Bari* (Cleveland Museum of Art) and *S. James* (Brooklyn Museum); the right hand panels *SS. George and Dominic* (both in the Metropolitan Museum of Art, New York).
>
> Of the innumerable critical comments on the present work we may extract from an article by Roger Fry in the Burlington Magazine of 1912 *(vide infra)* the following: "One of Crivelli's greatest designs, a fact which he himself seems to have recognized, since it occurs again, only reversed, in the Brussels "Madonna." Mr. Benson's [i.e. the present painting] is unquestionably the finer conception, if only because Crivelli has pressed into the service of his imaginative feeling even the design of the Virgin's brocaded robe, for the sharpness and tension of the movement of the head gets its value from the great diagonal line of the pattern."

Collection of Cardinal Fesch, Rome, 1845

Collection of G. H. Morland, Esq., London, 1863, no. 76

Collection of William Graham, Esq., London, 1886, no. 331

From P. & D. Colnaghi, London

Collection of Robert and Evelyn Benson, London

From Duveen Bros., Inc., New York

Exhibited at the Royal Academy, London, 1875, no. 182

Exhibited at the Royal Academy, London, 1887, no. 180

Exhibited at the New Gallery, London, 1894-95, no. 32

National Loan Exhibition, Grafton Galleries, London, 1909-10, no. 71, illus. in the catalogue

Early Venetian Exhibition, Burlington Fine Arts Club, London, 1912, no. 9, illus. in the catalogue, pl. 8

Recorded and illustrated in Rushforth, *Carlo Crivelli*, 1900, p. 46 and as frontispiece

Recorded in Lionello Venturi, *Le Origini della Pittura Veneziana*, 1907, pp. 195-97

Mentioned in Crowe and Cavalcaselle, *History of Painting in North Italy*, 1912, vol. I, p. 84, footnote

[Continued

MADONNA AND CHILD

CRIVELLI

Number Nine—Concluded]

Mentioned and illustrated by Tancred Borenius in *Rassegna d'Arte*, 1912, vol. XII, p. 88

Mentioned in Bernard Berenson, *The Study and Criticism of Italian Art*, 1912, vol. I, p. 102ff.

Recorded and illustrated in Lionello Venturi, *Storia dell'Arte Italiana*, 1914, vol. 7, pp. 362, 366

Recorded and illustrated in Franz Drey, *Carlo Crivelli und Seine Schule*, 1927, p. 127, pl. XXI

Illustrated in Lionello Venturi, *Italian Painting in America*, 1933, pl. 364

Recorded and illustrated in R. van Marle, *The Italian Schools of Painting*, 1936, vol. XVIII, pp. 7, 8, 9

Recorded in Pietro Zampetti, *Carlo Crivelli nelle Marche*, 1952, pp. 22, 69, no. 82

Recorded and illustrated in Bernard Berenson, *Italian Painters of the Renaissance (Venetian School)*, (Phaidon ed.), 1957, vol. I, p. 70, pl. 137

Mentioned by Pietro Zampetti in the foreword to the *Carlo Crivelli Loan Exhibition Catalogue*, Venice, 1961, p. XXXII

South Netherlands Master, Called the Master of S. Augustine

Scenes from the Life of S. Augustine

SOUTH NETHERLANDS MASTER, CALLED THE MASTER OF S. AUGUSTINE
BRUGES: CIRCA 1490

10. *SCENES FROM THE LIFE OF S. AUGUSTINE.* The composition is divided into five scenes. The central portion depicts Augustine being consecrated Bishop of Hippo: he is seated in a chapel before an altar with hands in prayer, receiving his mitre from the two consecrating prelates, as monks in white robes, and officials bearing tapers, croziers, chrism, etc., look on.

The side panels are: *upper left,* Augustine being ordained a priest, a mitred bishop standing before him within a vaulted baptistery; *lower left,* the youthful Augustine lectures from a pulpit to a group of Milanese citizens, prominent among them S. Ambrose, Bishop of Milan, and S. Monica, Augustine's mother. *Lower right,* Augustine, wearing a fur-trimmed red robe, stands with a group of scholars discussing philosophy, a secretary at rear recording the discourse; *upper right,* one of the most famous legends of the saint: One day, while engaged in writing his treatise, *De Trinitate,* Augustine walked along the shore, deep in thought, and came across a boy trying to fill a sand hole in the beach with water from the sea. The saint pointed out that this was an impossible task, since the water would always seep through, and the child replied that this would be no more impossible than attempting to explain the mystery of the Trinity.

Cradled panel: 54 x 59¾ *inches*

Note: From the article by Dr. Max J. Friedländer in *Art In America* of April 1937 (*vide infra*), we summarize the following informative comment: To the numbers of anonymous painters must be added "The Master of S. Augustine"; his chief work is an altarpiece with wings depicting legends from the life of S. Augustine. The centre panel is the Erickson painting. The inner side of the right wing was in the collection of the Earl of Ellenborough, and is now in the National Gallery, Dublin. The left wing is lost, and the subject matter can only be conjectured. The portrayal, in another panel by the same master, of the completed Bruges belfry (which was finished in 1482) indicates that the date of these works can be established as *circa* 1490. Dr. Friedländer also points out that there was a church of the Augustinian Order in Bruges, and that the complete triptych, devoted to the Legend of S. Augustine in great detail, was probably installed there.

Collection of the Comtesse de Béarn, Paris

Collection of Lord Exeter, Burghley, near Stamford, Northants.

From Steinmeyer, Cologne

Collection of Charles T. Yerkes, New York, 1910, no. 193 (*as by* Gerard David)

Collection of Fritz von Ansbach, Frankfurt-am-Main, 1910

From Julius Böhler, Munich

Collection of Fritz von Gans, Frankfurt-am-Main

From the Bachstitz Gallery, The Hague

[Continued

SCENES FROM THE LIFE OF S. AUGUSTINE

THE MASTER OF S. AUGUSTINE

Number Ten—Concluded]

Exhibition of Primitive Masters, Bachstitz Gallery, The Hague, 1922, no. 1, illus. in the catalogue

Mentioned by Wilhelm von Bode, in the preface to the *Catalogue of the Collection of Fritz von Gans,* n.d.

Mentioned by Dr. Georg Gronau, in the preface to the *Catalogue of the Bachstitz Gallery Collection, c.* 1922, vol. I, p. 3, and illus. pl. 2

Mentioned in *Cicerone,* June 1921, no. 11-12

Mentioned in *Cicerone,* October 1922, no. 20

Recorded and illustrated in S. Reinach, *Repertoire de Peintures,* vol. 6, 1923, p. 13 (*as* attributed to Simon Marmion)

Mentioned and illustrated in *Art News,* 1924, vol. XXII, no. 17

Described and illustrated by Max J. Friedländer, *The Bruges Master of S. Augustine* in *Art in America,* April 1937, vol. XXV, no. 2, pp. 46-54

Mentioned in Max J. Friedländer, *Die Altniederländische Malerei,* 1937, vol. XIV, p. 105

NUMBER ELEVEN

NUMBER ELEVEN

PIETRO VANNUCCI [PERUGINO]

S. Augustine with Members of the Confraternity of Perugia

PIETRO VANNUCCI [PERUGINO]   UMBRIAN: 1445-1523

11. *S. AUGUSTINE WITH MEMBERS OF THE CONFRATERNITY OF PERUGIA.* The saint is seated at full length upon a low stone bench, with his right hand raised in benediction; he wears a jeweled white mitre, an olive black robe and a brilliant ruby red cope lined in green, with gold-embroidered border; in his other hand is his crozier. In the background are four members of the religious order, wearing white hooded robes and kneeling in an attitude of prayer near their saintly patron. Behind these figures is a hilly landscape dominated by a fortified monastery; at left, feathery trees.   *Panel: 35 x 25 inches*

> *Note:* This painting was executed, according to Bombe, for the Oratory of the Brothers of S. Augustine in Perugia about 1500 (although it is not mentioned in the inventory of the friars), and is said to have been sold at auction by the fraternity in the seventeenth century. The physiognomy of the principal figure may be compared with that of the bishop (possibly S. Augustine) in the composition *Madonna and Child with Saints* in the Alte Pinakothek, Munich; see also, for the kneeling figures in the background, the *Madonna with Members of the Confraternity* still in Perugia.
>
> Lord Balniel and Sir Kenneth Clark in the catalogue of the 1930 exhibition at Burlington House *(vide infra)* contribute the following: "The figure of the saint is based on an earlier drawing . . . at Berlin. Drawings for the members of the confraternity, formerly in the Heseltine Collection, are published by Fischel, *Zeichnungen der Umbrer,* 1917, pp. 74, 122."

Painted about 1500

Collection of Lucien Bonaparte, Paris, 1815, no. 86

Collection of King William II of Holland, The Hague, 1851, no. 123

Collection of the Grand Duke of Saxe-Weimar, Weimar

From Cassirer, Amsterdam

Collection of Richard Weininger, Berlin, 1930

From Wildenstein & Co., Inc., New York

Exhibition of Italian Art, Royal Academy, London, 1930, no. 370

Recorded in Nieuwenhuis, *Galerie de Tableaux de Sa Majesté, le Roi des Pays-Bas,* 1843, no. 87

Recorded and illustrated in Bombe, *Perugino (Klassiker der Kunst),* 1914, no. 191

Recorded and illustrated in Gnoli, *Pietro Perugino,* 1923, p. 68, pl. 27

Mentioned by Bombe in *Jahrbuch für Kunstwissenschaft,* 1924, p. 137

Recorded in Lord Balniel and Kenneth Clark, eds., *A Commemorative Catalogue . . . London,* 1930, 1931, p. 84, no. 243

Recorded in Canuti, *Il Perugino,* 1931, vol. 1, p. 145, no. 6, and vol. 2, p. 349, no. 127

Recorded in Raymond van Marle, *The Italian Schools of Painting,* 1933, vol. XIV, pp. 362, 395-96

Recorded and illustrated in Rizzoli (ed.), *Tutta la Pittura del Perugino,* 1959, no. 104

Engraved by Griggi in *Choix de Gravures . . . de la Galerie Lucien Bonaparte,* 1812, no. 126

S. AUGUSTINE WITH MEMBERS OF THE
CONFRATERNITY OF PERUGIA

PERUGINO

NUMBER TWELVE

REMBRANDT HARMENSZ VAN RIJN

Portrait of an Old Man

REMBRANDT HARMENSZ VAN RIJN
DUTCH: 1606-1669

12. *PORTRAIT OF AN OLD MAN.* Half-length bearded figure of a gray haired man, wearing a loose brown robe, his hands folded before him; dark background. Signed at right centre REMBRANDT *f.*, and dated 1659.

Panel: 15 x 10½ inches

Note: This portrait, which was at one time known as *S. Matthew,* is undoubtedly one of the group of Jewish subjects painted by Rembrandt in his maturity. Jakob Rosenberg, in his work on the painter (*vide infra*) discusses (p. 59) the unconventionality of such representations in seventeenth century painting, and indicates that one of the reasons why Rembrandt took such interest in these people was that he lived at the edge of the Jewish quarter in Amsterdam; and in a broader perspective, that the artist's deepening religious attitude was primarily responsible for his intensive interest in the Jews as the authentic people of the Bible.

Dr. W. R. Valentiner, in a letter to the late Mr Erickson, dated Dec. 2, 1925, wrote of this picture in part as follows: "The old man from the Kappel collection dated 1659 is surely one of the most impressive and most freely painted portraits I know, of this last and great period of Rembrandt. It makes a most wonderful addition to your collection, representing as it does the latter art of the master, with all its deep and touching sentiment. . . ." This letter will be given to the purchaser.

Collection of Sir G. Douglas Clark, Bart., Penicuik, Scotland

Collection of R. Langton Douglas, Esq., London

Collection of Marcus Kappel, Berlin, 1913, no. 24

From the Bachstitz Gallery, The Hague

Exhibited in Berlin, 1914, no. 130

Rembrandt Exhibition, Detroit Institute of Arts, Detroit, Mich., 1930, no. 64, illus. in the catalogue

Exhibition, Man and His Years, Baltimore Museum of Art, Baltimore, Md., 1954, no. 40, illus. in the catalogue

Mentioned by Hofstede de Groot in *Onze Kunst,* Dec. 1909, p. 176

Recorded in Hofstede de Groot, *Catalogue Raisonné,* 1916, vol. VI, no. 367

Recorded and illustrated in W. R. Valentiner, *Rembrandt, Wiedergefundene Gemälde* (*Klassiker der Kunst* supplement), 1923, no. 93

Recorded and illustrated in W. R. Valentiner, *Rembrandt Paintings in America,* 1931, no. 144

Recorded and illustrated in Jakob Rosenberg, *Rembrandt,* 1948, no. 100

PORTRAIT OF AN OLD MAN

REMBRANDT

NUMBER THIRTEEN

Frans Hals

Man with a Herring (Pieter Cornelisz van der Morsch)

FRANS HALS   DUTCH: 1580-1666

13. *MAN WITH A HERRING (PIETER CORNELISZ VAN DER MORSCH)*. Half-length figure of a ruddy-faced man with mustache and chin beard, wearing a black robe with white ruff, turned to half-left, and glancing at the observer. In his right hand he holds a herring, and his other rests on a bale of straw. Inscribed on wall behind: WIE BEGEERT, and at upper right AETAT SVAE 73, and dated 1616 beneath the sitter's coat of arms.   34½ x 27½ *inches*

Pieter van der Morsch (1543-1629), a herring merchant, and the son of Cornelisz van der Morsch, was an official messenger of the Corporation of Leyden; he was also a member of the Chamber of Rhetoric, and was at one time bailiff of the city of Haarlem. His nickname was 'Piero,' and he seems to have had the reputation of being something of a prankster; thus in the present portrait he is shown as an eminent Haarlem burgher, who was also an armiger, yet making fun of his dignity by the offer of the herring, with the words *Wie begeert* (who wants it?). An eighteenth century watercolor drawing by Vincent van der Vinne, after this portrait, was in the collection of Frits Lugt.

Collection Van Tol, Soeterwoude, near Leyden, 1779, no. 8

Collection of Barend Kooy, Amsterdam, 1820, no. 38

Collection of C. H. Hodges, *et al*, Amsterdam, 1838, no. 294

Collection of J. A. Töpfer, Amsterdam, 1841, no. 28

From Martin Colnaghi, London

Collection of the Earl of Northbrook, Stratton, Micheldever, Hants, 1889, no. 61

From Duveen Bros., Inc., New York

Exhibition, Fifty Paintings by Frans Hals, Detroit Institute of Arts, Detroit, Mich., 1935, no. 1, illus. in the catalogue

Described in Hofstede de Groot, *Catalogue Raisonné*, 1910, vol. III, no. 205

Recorded and illustrated in W. von Bode and M. J. Binder, *Frans Hals, Sein Leben und Seine Werke*, 1914, vol. I, no. 89, pl. 43

Recorded and illustrated in W. R. Valentiner, *Frans Hals (Klassiker der Kunst)*, 1923, p. 11

Mentioned and illustrated in *International Studio*, Aug. 1928, p. 61

Illustrated in *Art News*, Jan. 12, 1935

Recorded and illustrated in W. R. Valentiner, *Frans Hals Paintings in America*, 1936, no. 2

MAN WITH A HERRING

HALS

NUMBER FOURTEEN

REMBRANDT HARMENSZ VAN RIJN

Prince Frederick Henry of Orange, Governor of the Netherlands

REMBRANDT HARMENSZ VAN RIJN   DUTCH: 1606-1669

14. *PRINCE FREDERICK HENRY OF ORANGE, GOVERNOR OF THE NETHERLANDS.* Half-length figure of a young man with long tightly curled auburn hair, standing to right and looking directly at the observer; he wears a watered silk coat of pale grayish-pink with a broad white collar and cuffs, and holds before him a black steeple hat; greenish background. Signed at lower right REMBRANDT *f.*, and dated, almost illegibly, 1637.   *Panel: 32 x 28 inches*

Frederick Henry (1584-1647) was the youngest child of William the Silent, of the house of Orange; he succeeded his brother Maurice of Nassau in 1625, as Stadtholder of the Netherlands and Captain and Admiral-General of the Republic.

Note: The identification of the sitter appears to have been first made by Dr. W. R. Valentiner in 1925, older works describing it as *Portrait of a Young Man*, etc. The subject was Governor of the Netherlands in the great years of the Dutch Republic, and the portrait is, according to the same authority, very likely identical with that mentioned in the collection of the sitter's wife, Amalia of Solms, in 1667.

Collection Proley, Paris, 1787

Collection of Prince Nicholas Gagarine, Moscow

Rembrandt Exhibition, Detroit Institute of Arts, Detroit, Mich., 1930, no. 28, illus. in the catalogue

Described and illustrated in W. von Bode and C. Hofstede de Groot, *The Complete Works of Rembrandt*, 1906, vol. VIII, no 570, illus. p. 102 (*as* A Young Man in Profile)

Recorded and illustrated in W. R. Valentiner, *Rembrandt, Des Meisters Gemälde (Klassiker der Kunst)*, 1908, no. 217

Recorded in Hofstede de Groot, *Catalogue Raisonné*, 1916, vol. VI, no. 751

Recorded and illustrated in Maldran, *Rembrandt's Paintings*, n.d., p. 190, pl. 120

Recorded and illustrated in W. R. Valentiner, *Rembrandt Paintings in America*, 1931, no. 62

PRINCE FREDERICK HENRY OF ORANGE

REMBRANDT

NUMBER FIFTEEN

Louis Tocqué

Mlle Suzanne le Mercier (Mlle Plainval)

LOUIS TOCQUE FRENCH: 1696-1772

15. *MLLE SUZANNE LE MERCIER (MLLE PLAINVAL). Three-quarter-length figure of a handsome woman, wearing a fur-trimmed silvery gray mantle over a lacy white cap and dark turquoise velvet dress; she is seated in a caned fauteuil before a landscape background.* *32 x 25½ inches*

Mlle Suzanne le Mercier, known as Mlle Plainval (1689-1757) was the daughter of Olivier le Mercier (1643-1701) and Suzanne de Monchy (1657-1726). She was a lady of great wealth, but never married; adopted her nephew Jean-Baptiste-Louis de Plainval (*vide infra*), and her niece Mme Marchart.

Note: This painting descended in the Plainval family, and for that reason the sitter had been identified as Mlle Plainval, who adopted the first owner of this portrait. According to the original record of the picture from Messrs Wildenstein, the painting is signed and dated 1745 on the back of the canvas, the signature and date now being covered by the relining.

Painted in 1745

Collection of Jean-Baptiste-Louis de Plainval, nephew of the sitter

Collection of Comte Paul de Plainval

Collection of Comte Fernand de Plainval, Paris, 1911

From Wildenstein et Cie, Paris

Collection of James and Charles Chauncey Stillman, New York, 1927

From Wildenstein & Co., Inc., New York

Exhibited at the Salon, Paris, 1745, no. 75

Exhibition of Eighteenth Century French Paintings, Union League Club, New York, 1931, no. 6

Exhibited at the Fogg Art Museum, Cambridge, Mass., 1931

Recorded and illustrated in Comte Arnauld Doria, *Louis Tocqué*, 1921, p. 116, no. 167, and p. 205, fig. 49

SUZANNE LE MERCIER

TOCQUE

Jean Honoré Fragonard

La Liseuse

JEAN HONORE FRAGONARD   FRENCH: 1732-1806

16. *LA LISEUSE.* Depicting a young woman, her upswept auburn hair tied with
a rose ribbon, seated propped upon pillows in profile to left, reading a book, which
she holds daintily in her right hand as she rests her arm on a railing; she wears a
saffron yellow dress with a white ruff and ribbons at the corsage.   *32 x 25½ inches*

> *Note:* This is one of a group of paintings of young women executed by
> Fragonard about 1776; in the words of M. Georges Wildenstein ". . . their eyes
> downcast, engaged in reading a book or letter, and showing by a play of the features,
> a smile, or an air of sadness, the joy or vexation which their reading brings them.
> This kind of picture, though the subject is at first glance a surprising one, was then
> in fashion . . . we know of no artist more successful than Fragonard at painting
> these studious ladies, these girls reading letters, notes and pamphlets."

Painted about 1776

Vente Anonyme, Feb. 7, 1777, no. 15

Collection Leroy de Senneville, Paris, April 5, 1780, no. 59

Collection Duquesnoy, Paris, March 10, 1803, no. 19

Vente Anonyme, April 26, 1844, no. 14

Collection of the Marquis de Cypierre, Paris, 1845, no. 55

Collection of the Comte de Kergolay, Paris

Collection of E. Cronier, Paris, 1905, no. 8

Collection of Dr. Tuffier, Paris

From Wildenstein & Co., Inc., New York

Exposition Cent Portraits de Femmes, Jeu de Paume, Paris, 1909, no. 64, illus. in
the catalogue

Exposition, L'Art Français du XVIII° Siècle, Royal Academy of Arts, Berlin,
1910, no. 51, illus. in the catalogue, p. 54

Exposition Fragonard, Pavillon de Marsan, Paris, 1921, no. 56, illus. in the catalogue

Exhibition, Three French Reigns, Sir Philip Sassoon's Residence, London, 1933,
no. 517

Exhibition of French Painting and Sculpture of the Eighteenth Century, Metropolitan Museum of Art, New York, 1935-36, no. 45, illus. in the catalogue

Jubilee Loan Exhibition, Masterpieces from Museums and Private Collections, Wildenstein Galleries, New York, 1951, no. 29, illus. in the catalogue

Recorded in Henri Portalis, *Honoré Fragonard, Sa Vie et Son Oeuvre,* 1889, p. 282

Illustrated in *Les Arts,* 1905, p. 15

[*Continued*

LA LISEUSE

FRAGONARD

Number Sixteen—Concluded]

Mentioned by G. Brière and P. A. Lemoisne, *Portraits de L'Ecole Française du XVIII° Siècle*, in *Bulletin de L'Art Français*, 1909, p. 129

Illustrated in Georges Grappe, *Fragonard Peintre de L'Amour au XVIII° Siècle*, 1913, vol. I, p. 78

Recorded and illustrated in Pierre de Nolhac, *J. H. Fragonard*, 1918 and 1931, pp. 146-47

Mentioned by Georges Wildenstein, *L'Exposition Fragonard au Pavillon de Marsan*, in *La Renaissance*, July 1921, p. 362

Mentioned by Alfred Frankfurter, *Thirty-five Portraits from American Collections*, in *Art News*, May 1931, p. 4

Recorded and illustrated in Georges Wildenstein, *The Paintings of Fragonard* (Phaidon ed.), 1960, no. 391, pl. 80

NUMBER SEVENTEEN

Hubert Robert

Le Pont de Pierre

HUBERT ROBERT   FRENCH: 1733-1808

17. *LE PONT DE PIERRE.* On a rocky promontory in the foreground, a rustic youth sprawls fishing in a lake which cascades over jagged rocks before him; beside him stands a young woman holding a child and gesturing toward her companion. The group is seen before an arched stone bridge, which is crowned at right with an ancient Gothic tower, and in the distance the mountainous shore of the lake is visible beneath a clouded summer sky. Signed at lower right on the bridge H. ROBERT, and dated 1796.   *Oval: 32¼ x 25 inches*

> *Note:* This and the following painting were executed for insertion in an important *boiserie* in a room in the Stroganoff Palace at St. Petersburg.

Companion to the following

Collection of Count Paul Stroganoff, St. Petersburg

From Wildenstein & Co., Inc., New York

Exhibition of Paintings and Drawings by Hubert Robert, Wildenstein Galleries, New York, 1935, no. 24

Recorded in Louis Réau, *L'Art Français dans les Musées Russes*, p. 54

Recorded in Louis Réau, *L'Histoire de l'Expansion de l'Art Français Moderne*, p. 204

Recorded by Louis Réau, *L'Oeuvre de H. Robert en Russie* in the *Gazette des Beaux Arts*, Jan. 1934, p. 173ff.

LE PONT DE PIERRE

ROBERT

NUMBER EIGHTEEN

Hubert Robert

Au Bois

HUBERT ROBERT   FRENCH: 1733-1808

18. *AU BOIS.* In the left foreground, beside a blasted tree, an amorous rustic couple are seen resting before a thick wood, through which a tunnel-like opening leads into the distance where a rugged mountainous landscape is visible; near the couple are a picnic basket, the youth's staff and hat, and two lambs. Signed at lower centre H. ROBERT, and dated 1796.   *Oval: 32½ x 25½ inches*

See note to the preceding.

Companion to the preceding

Collection of Count Paul Stroganoff, St. Petersburg

From Wildenstein & Co., Inc., New York

Exhibition of Paintings and Drawings by Hubert Robert, Wildenstein Galleries, New York, 1935, no. 25

Recorded in Louis Réau, *L'Art Français dans les Musées Russes,* p. 54

Recorded in Louis Réau, *L'Histoire de l'Expansion de l'Art Français Moderne,* p. 204

Recorded by Louis Réau, *L'Oeuvre de H. Robert en Russie* in the *Gazette des Beaux Arts,* Jan. 1934, p. 173ff.

AU BOIS

ROBERT

NUMBER NINETEEN

JEAN MARC NATTIER

La Marquise de Baglion, as Flora

JEAN MARC NATTIER   FRENCH: 1685-1766

19. *LA MARQUISE DE BAGLION, AS FLORA.* Almost-full-length figure of a beautiful young woman, wearing a décolleté white dress and flowing pale blue mantle; she is seated before a clouded dawn sky, and holds a spray of flowers in her hand, other blossoms strewn on her lap and tied at her sleeve. Signed at lower right NATTIER, *pinxit,* and dated 1746.   54 x 41¾ *inches*

Angélique Louise-Sophie d'Allouville de Louville, Marquise de Baglion (1710-1756), was the daughter of Charles Augustin d'Allouville, Marquis de Louville, a gentleman-in-waiting to the King of Spain and Lieutenant-General of his armies, and of Hyacinthe-Sophie de Bechameil de Nointel. She married Pierre François-Marie de Baglion, Comte de la Salle, on June 10, 1733. Their only daughter, Françoise Sophie Scholastique de Baglion later became the Marquise de Roure. See la Chesnaye Desbois, *Dictionnaire,* 1863, vol. II, pp. 187-88.

The sitter was one of the great beauties of her day, and the present portrait has been considered by many to be one of the finest painted in the eighteenth century. It inspired a madrigal of eight verses written by L. Roger-Milès; a brochure, containing the history of the painting and the text of the madrigal, will be given to the purchaser.

Collection of the Comtesse Armand, *née* Gontaud-Biron

Collection of the Marquis de Chaponay, Paris

Collection of M. Nicolas Ambatielos, London

From Wildenstein & Co., Inc., New York

Exhibited at the Salon, Paris, 1746, p. 20, no. 70 in the catalogue (See Nolhac, p. 275)

Exhibition, One Hundred Masterpieces, Paris, 1892, no. 28

Exposition, Cent Portraits de Femmes, Paris, 1909, no. 85, illus. in the catalogue

Exhibition of Eighteenth Century French Paintings, Union League Club of New York, New York, 1931

Recorded in Bélier de la Chavignerie & Auvray, *Dictionnaire des Peintres,* p. 152

Recorded in L. Vaillat & R. Dell, *One Hundred Masterpieces,* no. 19

Recorded in P. de Nolhac, *Nattier, Peintre de la Cour de Louis XV,* 1905, pp. 157 and 277, and 1925, pp. 190, 247 and 275, illus. opp. p. 190

Mentioned and illustrated by Ch. Saunier in *Les Arts,* 1909, p. 10, no. 91

Mentioned by M. Tourneux in the *Gazette des Beaux-Arts,* 1909, p. 488

Mentioned by A. Dayot in *L'Art et les Artistes,* pp. 52 and 54

Recorded and illustrated in Esther Singleton, *Old World Masters in New World Collections,* 1929, p. 288ff.

Recorded and illustrated in Wilhelm R. Valentiner, *Das Unbekannte Meisterwerk in Oeffentlichen and Privaten Sammlungen,* 1930, no. 78

LA MARQUISE DE BAGLION, AS FLORA

NATTIER

NUMBER TWENTY

THOMAS GAINSBOROUGH, R.A.

Dorothea, Lady Eden

THOMAS GAINSBOROUGH, R. A.   BRITISH: 1727-1788

20. *DOROTHEA, LADY EDEN.* Half-length figure of an attractive woman facing slightly to left, her powdered hair arranged high upon her head and falling in two ringlets about her neck; she wears a filmy grayish-white low-cut dress enhanced at the bodice with pearls; her hands are folded before her, clasping a fringed gold shawl draped loosely over her arms; dark crimson draperies at left.

30¼ x 25 inches

Dorothea, Lady Eden, of Windlestone Hall, Durham, was the daughter of Peter Johnson, Esq., Recorder of York. In 1767 she became the second wife of Sir John Eden, 4th Baronet. She died in 1792, survived by eight children, her eldest son succeeding his father as 5th Baronet in 1812.

Painted about 1770-75

Collection of Mrs Eden Kaye Greville, a descendant of the sitter

Collection of James Price, Esq.

Collection of Sir Julian Goldsmid, Bart., M.P., London

From Thomas Agnew & Sons, London

From Charles Wertheimer, London

Collection of Mrs John W. Simpson, New York

From Duveen Bros., Inc., New York

Royal Academy Exhibition, Burlington House, London, 1878 and 1887

Gainsborough Exhibition, Grosvenor Galleries, London, 1885, no. 114

Recorded in Sir W. Armstrong, *Gainsborough and His Place in English Art*, 1898, p. 194

Illustrated in Lord Ronald Sutherland Gower, *Thomas Gainsborough*, 1903, p. 20

Recorded and illustrated in William B. Boulton, *Thomas Gainsborough, His Life, Work, Friends and Sitters*, 1907, p. 102

Mentioned and illustrated in *International Studio*, Aug. 1928, p. 61

Recorded in Ellis K. Waterhouse, *Gainsborough*, 1958, p. 65, no. 230

Engraved by G. H. Every, 1866

DOROTHEA, LADY EDEN

GAINSBOROUGH

NUMBER TWENTY-ONE

SIR HENRY RAEBURN, R.A.

Quintin McAdam as a Boy

SIR HENRY RAEBURN, R. A.   SCOTTISH: 1756-1823

21. *QUINTIN McADAM AS A BOY*. Full-length figure of a fair-haired boy
wearing a chocolate brown jacket, straw yellow vest, white ruffled shirt and buff
breeches. He stands in a rocky landscape and holds a riding crop in his right hand,
and a high-crowned black hat in his left.   *61 x 47¼ inches*

Quintin McAdam (1805-1826) was the only son of Quintin McAdam of
Craigengillan, Scotland, to whom Robert Burns addressed an "Epistle to Mr. Mac-
Adam of Craigengillan," in which he refers to him as "young Dunaskin's Laird."
Dunaskin is a village near Craigengillan.

The elder McAdam's wife was a member of the MacEwen family, and after
her husband's death, the picture descended in the MacEwen line.

Painted in 1817

Collection of the MacEwen family of Camlarg, Craigengillan, Ayrshire, N.B.

From Thos. Agnew & Sons, Inc., New York

Recorded and illustrated in Esther Singleton, *Old World Masters in New World
Collections*, 1929, p. 416

Recorded and illustrated in Wilhelm R. Valentiner, *Das Unbekannte Meisterwerk
in Oeffentlichen und Privaten Sammlungen*, 1930, no. 101

90

QUINTIN McADAM AS A BOY

RAEBURN

NUMBER TWENTY-TWO

GEORGE ROMNEY

Mrs James Lowther (née Mary Codrington)

32 000

GEORGE ROMNEY   BRITISH: 1734-1802

22. *MRS JAMES LOWTHER (née MARY CODRINGTON)*. Seated half-length figure of a pretty young woman, turned to half-left and gazing at the observer; she wears a grayish-black dress with a ruffled lawn collar and a white "mushroom" bonnet trimmed with a profusion of maroon ribbons; her blue-gloved hands are clasped before her; clouded sky background.   *30 x 25 inches*

The sitter was the wife of Colonel James Lowther, Equerry to H.R.H. the Duke of Gloucester, a son of George III. She sat to Romney, July 29, 1786.

Painted in 1786

Collection of Lieut.-Col. Henry Lowther, great-grandson of the sitter

Collection of G. A. Lowther, Esq.

From Duveen Bros., Inc., New York

Exhibited at the Grafton Gallery, London, 1900, no. 28

Mentioned in the Rev. John Romney's MS. list, 1830

Recorded in H. Ward & W. Roberts, *Romney*, 1904, vol. II, pp. 96-97

MRS JAMES LOWTHER

ROMNEY

NUMBER TWENTY-THREE

Sɪʀ Hᴇɴʀʏ Rᴀᴇʙᴜʀɴ, R.A.

Capt. David Kinloch, R.N.

SIR HENRY RAEBURN, R. A.   SCOTTISH: 1756-1823

23. *CAPT. DAVID KINLOCH, R.N.* Half-length figure of a portly gentleman, with ruddy complexion and powdered white hair, looking at the observer; he wears a double-breasted snuff brown jacket with brass buttons, and white frilled jabot.

30 x 24¾ inches

Captain David Kinloch, R.N. (1736-1818), served in the East Indies for many years, his last command being H.M.S. "Swan"; he succeeded his father as the fifth Laird of Gourdie in Perthshire N.B., in 1743.

Note: MS endorsements on photographs by Charles Kinloch, Esq., a former owner, and Wm. Roberts, dated 1922 and 1923, respectively, will be given to the purchaser.

Collection of Capt. David Kinloch, Gourdie House, Perthshire, son of the sitter

Collection of Colonel David Kinloch, Perthshire, his son

Collection of Charles G. Kinloch, Esq., Vernon, B.C., his son

Loan Exhibition of Masterpieces of Painting, Museum of Fine Arts, Montreal, Que., 1942, no. 92

CAPT. DAVID KINLOCH, R.N.

RAEBURN

NUMBER TWENTY-FOUR

GEORGE ROMNEY

The Young Squire

GEORGE ROMNEY

24. *THE YOUNG SQUIRE.* Three-quarter-length standing figure of a fair-haired lad, wearing a black stove-pipe hat, scarlet jacket with white lace collar and buff trousers, holding a stick and a hoop; sky background.   24¾ x 20 *inches*

The sitter was Master Augustus Henry Bosanquet. In 1795, Romney gave no less than twenty-five sittings to the Bosanquet family; Charles Napier Lawrence (*vide infra*) was a descendant of this family.

Painted about 1795

Collection of the Bosanquet family, bankers in London

Collection of the Hon. Charles Napier Lawrence, Auchennove, Aberdeenshire

Collection of Lady de Bathe

From Paul E. Cremetti, London

THE YOUNG SQUIRE

ROMNEY